SPECIAL SCHOOL EDITION

HOLIDAY EXPRESS

GRADE 4

AF650332

SCHOLASTIC
New York Toronto London Auckland
Sydney New Delhi Hong Kong

Interior illustrations by Robert Alley, Abbey Carter, Maxie Chambliss, Sue Dennen, Shelley Dieterichs, Jane Dippold, Julie Durrell, Rusty Fletcher, James Hale, Mike Moran, Sherry Neidigh, Cary Pillo, Carol Tiernon and Lynn Vineyard

ISBN-13 978-93-5275-796-1

Printed at Polykam offset Naraina New Delhi 110028

Table of Contents

Dear Parent:

Congratulations! You hold in your hands an exceptional educational tool that will give your child a head start into the coming school year.

Inside this book, you'll find practice pages that will help your child review and learn reading and writing skills, grammar, addition and subtraction, and so much more! *Holiday Express* is divided into 6 weeks, with two practice pages for each day of the week, Monday to Friday. However, feel free to use the pages in any order that your child would like. Here are other features you'll find inside:

- A weekly **incentive chart** to motivate and reward your child for his or her efforts.
- Suggestions for fun, creative **learning activities** you can do with your child each week.
- A **recommended reading list** of age-appropriate books that you and your child can read throughout the summer.

We hope you and your child will have a lot of fun as you work together to complete this workbook.

Enjoy!
The Editors

Terrific Tips for Using This Book

1 Pick a good time for your child to work on the activities. You may want to do it around mid-morning, or early afternoon when your child is not too tired.

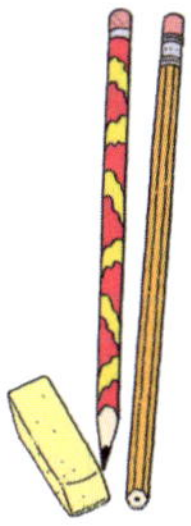

2 Make sure your child has all the supplies he or she needs, such as pencils and markers. Set aside a special place for your child to work.

3 At the beginning of each week, discuss with your child how many minutes a day he or she would like to read. Write the goal at the top of the incentive chart for the week. (We recommend that your child entering fourth grade read 20 to 25 minutes a day.)

5 Encourage your child to complete the worksheet, but don't force the issue. While you may want to ensure that your child succeeds, it's also important that your child maintain a positive and relaxed attitude toward school and learning.

6 After you've given your child a few minutes to look over the practice pages he or she will be working on, ask your child to tell you his or her plan of action: "Tell me about what we're doing on these pages." Hearing the explanation aloud can provide you with insight into your child's thinking processes. Can he or she complete the work independently? With guidance? If your child needs support from a family member, try offering choices regarding with whom he or she will be working. Providing choices is an approach that can help boost your child's confidence and help him or her feel more ownership of the work to be done.

Skill-Building Activities for Any Time

The following activities are designed to complement the ten weeks of practice pages in this book. These activities don't take more than a few minutes to complete and are just a handful of ways in which you can enrich and enliven your child's learning. Use the activities to take advantage of the time you might ordinarily disregard—for example, standing in line or waiting at a bus stop. You'll be working to practice key skills and have fun together at the same time.

Finding Real-Life Connections

One of the reasons for schooling is to help children function out in the real world, to empower them with the abilities they'll truly need. So why not put those developing skills into action by enlisting your child's help with reading a map, following a recipe, checking grocery receipts and so on. He or she can apply reading, writing, science and math skills in important and practical ways, connecting what he or she is learning with everyday tasks.

An Eye for Patterns

A red-brick sidewalk, a beaded necklace, a Sunday newspaper—all show evidence of structure and organisation. You can help your child recognise something's structure or organisation by observing and talking about patterns they see. Your child will apply his or her developing ability to spot patterns across all school subject areas, including alphabet letter formation (writing), attributes of shapes and solids (geometry) and characteristics of narrative stories (reading). Being able to notice patterns is a skill shared by effective readers and writers, scientists and mathematicians.

Journals as Learning Tools

Most of us associate journal writing with reading comprehension, but having your child keep a journal can help you keep up with his or her developing skills in other academic areas as well—from adding fractions to combining sentences. To get started, provide your child with several sheets of paper, folded in half and stapled together. Explain that he or she will be writing and/or drawing in the journal to complement the practice pages completed each week. The journal is another tool you both can use to monitor progress of skills newly learned or practiced, or those that need improvement. Before moving on to another set of practice pages, take a few minutes to read and discuss that week's journal entries together.

Promote Reading at Home

- Let your child catch you in the act of reading for pleasure, whether you like reading science fiction novels or do-it-yourself magazines. Store them someplace that encourages you to read in front of your child and **demonstrate that reading is an activity you enjoy**. For example, locate your reading materials on the coffee table instead of your nightstand.
- Set aside a family reading time. By designating a reading time each week, your family is assured an opportunity to discuss with each other what you're reading. You can, for example, share a funny quote from an article. Or your child can tell you his or her favourite part of a story. The key is to **make a family tradition of reading and sharing books** of all kinds together.
- **Put together collections of reading materials** your child can access easily. Gather them in baskets or bins that you can place in the family room, the car and your child's bedroom. You can refresh your child's library by borrowing materials from your community's library, buying used books, or swapping books and magazines with friends and neighbors.

Skills Review and Practice

Educators have established learning standards for math and language arts. Listed below are some of the important skills that will help your child review and prepare for the coming school year so that he or she is better prepared to meet these learning standards.

Math

Skills Your Child Will Review

- identifying fractions
- demonstrating knowledge of addition and subtraction facts
- adding 3-digit numbers without regrouping
- subtracting 2-digit numbers without regrouping
- identifying coin and rupee values; logic

Skills Your Child Will Practice to Prepare for Grade Four

- solving word problems
- matching equivalent fractions
- identifying numerators and denominators of fractions
- adding 4-digit numbers without regrouping
- adding and subtracting decimals
- demonstrating knowledge of multiplication facts
- multiplying 2-digit and 3-digit numbers; logic
- dividing with remainders
- adding simple fractions with like denominators
- finding area and perimeter (e.g., feet, yards)
- adding and subtracting decimals; money
- identifying attributes (e.g., angles, sides)
- reading and using data from a table and chart

Language Arts

Skills Your Child Will Review

- proofreading (e.g., meaning, spelling, sentence variety and grammar)
- expanding and combining sentences
- using parts of speech in written compositions (e.g., common nouns, proper nouns, plural nouns, pronouns, present- and past-tense verbs, adjectives, prepositions)
- punctuating (e.g., possessives, quotation marks, contractions)
- writing in upper- and lowercase cursive letters
- writing cursive numerals 0–9
- demonstrating knowledge of level-appropriate reading vocabulary (e.g., homophones, synonyms, antonyms, prefixes [un-], compound words, analogies, word relationships)

Skills Your Child Will Practice to Prepare for Grade Four

- Using prewriting strategies (e.g., graphic organisers, outlines)
- writing for a purpose (e.g., a news story, expository paragraph, persuasive paragraph, descriptive paragraph)
- using topic sentences
- writing in paragraph form
- diagramming sentences to demonstrate understanding of parts of speech and sentence structures
- understanding an author's purpose for writing (e.g., to inform, persuade)
- recognising and identifying literary devices (e.g., simile, metaphor)
- demonstrating knowledge of level-appropriate reading vocabulary (e.g., compound words, contractions, idioms and so on)
- demonstrating knowledge of level-appropriate identification of root words (e.g., *pos, phon, photo, port, pop*)
- establishing a purpose for reading (e.g., standardised test taking)
- identifying story elements
- using graphic organisers to interpret information
- understanding different techniques convey messages (e.g., comics, advertising)

Helping Your Child Get Ready: Week 1

These are the skills your child will be working on this week.

Math
- addition of 4-digit numbers without regrouping
- subtraction of 2-digit numbers without regrouping
- identifying multiplication patterns

Reading
- following directions
- identifying fact and opinion
- comparing and contrasting

Writing
- compound sentences

Vocabulary
- suffixes
- analogies

Here are some activities you and your child might enjoy.

Newspaper Treasure Hunt In this special hunt, your child looks for various "treasures" in a newspaper article. The treasures are letters or symbols to which you've assigned a value. For example, a *z* might be worth ₹10 and an exclamation point might be ₹5. Have your child search an article to find out how valuable its "treasure" is.

Two-Minute Lists Give your child two minutes to list as many words as he or she can think of that include double letters.

What's in a Name? Have your child research his or her name. Have him or her find out what the name means. Then tell your child the story of how you chose it. Encourage him or her to find out the meanings of other family members' names as well.

Leaf Survey What kinds of leaves are there in your neighborhood? Have your child do a leaf survey. He or she can collect leaves, use reference books to identify them and then make a list of all the different trees found in your area.

Your child might enjoy reading the following books:

The Magic Faraway Tree
by Enid Blyton

Moody and the Bad Luck Charm
by Megan McDonald

Geronimo Stilton: Super Chef Contest
by Geronimo Stilton

______________________ **'s Incentive Chart: Week 1**

Name Here

This week, I plan to read __________ minutes each day.

CHART YOUR PROGRESS HERE.

Week 1	Day 1	Day 2	Day 3	Day 4	Day 5
 I read for...	minutes	minutes	minutes	minutes	minutes
Put a sticker to show you completed each day's work.					

Congratulations!

Wow! You did a great job this week!

Place sticker here.

Parent or Caregiver's Signature ______________________________

Who Said What?

Many words end with a suffix that means "one who" or "one who does an action."

astronom**er**	merch**ant**	superintend**ent**	invent**or**	dent**ist**
librar**ian**	pharmac**ist**	photograph**er**	edit**or**	wait**er**

Read the sentences. Write the word from the box that identifies who said what.

1. **"Your prescription is ready," said the ____________________.**
2. **"Would you like fries, mashed, or baked potatoes?" asked the ____________________.**
3. **"I am canceling classes today," the school ____________________ decided.**
4. **"These watches were imported from Germany," explained the ____________________.**
5. **"Star system Alpha Centauri is 4.3 light-years away," explained the ____________________.**
6. **"The fine for the overdue books is ₹ 5," stated the ____________________.**
7. **"Face the camera and smile," instructed the ____________________.**
8. **"This incredible engine will revolutionise transportation," explained the ____________________.**
9. **"It took two years to prepare this book for publication," said the ____________________.**
10. **"You have a small cavity in this back molar," said the ____________________.**

What do you want to be when you are an adult? What about your friends? Take a survey to find out. On another sheet of paper, list all the careers suggested.

A New Challenge

When you write, you may want to show how the ideas in two simple sentences are related. You can combine the two sentences by using a comma and the conjunctions and, but, *or* or *to show the connection.* And *shows a link between the ideas,* but *shows a contrast and* or *shows a choice. The new sentence is called a* **compound sentence**.

My sister wants to join a football team. My parents aren't so happy about it.
My sister wants to join a football team, but **my parents aren't so happy about it.**

Annie is determined. Her friends think she'd make a great place kicker.
Annie is determined and **her friends think she'd make a great place kicker.**

Should Annie play football? Should she try something else?
Should Annie play football, or **should she try something else?**

Combine each pair of sentences. Use *and, but,* or *or* to show the connection between the ideas and make a compound sentence.

1. **My sister Annie has always participated in sports. Many say she's a natural athlete.**

___

___

2. **Soccer, basketball and softball are fun. She wanted a new challenge.**

___

___

3. **My sister talked to my brother and me. We were honest with her.**

___

___

4. **I told Annie to go for it. My brother told her to stick with soccer or basketball.**

___

___

5. **Will Dad convince her to try skiing? Will he suggest ice skating?**

___

___

Continue the story about Annie's choice on another sheet of paper. Include some compound sentences to tell what happens. Make sure your sentences begin and end correctly. Remember to check for spelling errors.

Picking Pairs

For each number, a line connects two things that go together. Find two other things that go together in the same way. Draw a line to connect them.

1. imaginary — number
   ban — make-believe
   allow — forbid

5. core — see
   time — hear
   here — corps

2. secret — midnight
   huge — tiny
   solid — liquid

6. snake — mammal
   tiger — jungle
   skin — reptile

3. clap — permit
   prevent — applaud
   allow — pretend

7. perfect — flawless
   puppy — stare
   stroll — walk

4. terrier — retriever
   lime — strawberry
   penguin — crowd

8. chair — candle
   wick — soft
   cord — lamp

Tell a family member how the pairs you matched go together.

Majestic Mountains

Add. Use the code to name four different mountain ranges.

N	6,348
R	8,789
A	5,063
I	7,695
O	2,429
K	5,642
E	7,483
C	3,012
Y	2,351
Z	5,234
L	3,721
U	6,704
P	3,827
S	8,749
D	4,907

2,033 + 3,030	2,411 + 1,310	2,504 + 1,323	4,328 + 4,421	
4,258 + 4,531	1,326 + 1,103	1,012 + 2,000	2,321 + 3,321	1,231 + 1,120
1,204 + 1,225	2,113 + 3,121	2,042 + 3,021	3,746 + 5,043	4,131 + 1,511
4,053 + 1,010	2,216 + 4,132	2,506 + 2,401	6,471 + 1,012	7,326 + 1,423

Fun With Words

Follow the directions to play each word game.

1. A palindrome is a word that is spelled the same forward or backward. Write each word backward. Circle each word that is a palindrome. Put an *X* on each word that is not.

wow ____________

dad ____________

mom ____________

funny ____________

noon ____________

tall ____________

deed ____________

2. Some words imitate the noise that they stand for. For example, when you say "pop," it sounds like a popping sound! That is called onomatopoeia. Unscramble each noise word. Write it correctly.

seechrc ____________

owp ____________

plurs ____________

mobo ____________

lckic ____________

zzisel ____________

chnucr ____________

3. Homophones are words that sound alike when you say them but are spelled differently and have different meanings. For example, *see* and *sea* are homophones. Draw a line to match each pair of homophones.

knot	flew
break	soar
flu	not
sore	write
right	road
rode	brake

4. Add or subtract letters from each word to change it into another word. Write the new word.

peach – ch + r = ____________

shirt – irt + oe = ____________

sports – p – rts + ccer = ____________

love – ove + ike = ____________

stove – st + n = ____________

chicken – c – ick = ____________

brother – bro + nei = ____________

Some names sound funny when you pronounce them backward. For example, Carol would be pronounced Lorac and Jason would be pronounced Nosaj! Write your name and each of your family members' names backward. Then pronounce each name. Are any of the names palindromes?

TV Commercials

When you watch TV, you see a lot of commercials advertising different products. The people making the commercial want you to buy their product, so they make it sound as good as possible. Some of the things they say are facts, which can be proven. Other things are just the advertiser's opinion about how good the product is or how it will make you feel. Read each advertisement below. Write an *F* in the box beside each fact and an *O* in the box beside each opinion. The first one is done for you.

Eat at Billy Bob's Burgers.

[O] Best burgers in town

[F] Made with chicken

Drive an XJ-80 Sports Car today.

[ ] You'll never want to drive your old car again.

[ ] Available in black, red and silver

You'll be the Coolest Kid on Your Block with a Pair of Xtreme In-Line Skates! [ ]

[ ] On sale for ₹1799.99

Sky-Diving Adventure Video Game

[ ] Joystick sold separately

[ ] You'll have hours and hours of fun!

Elastic Man, the Movie

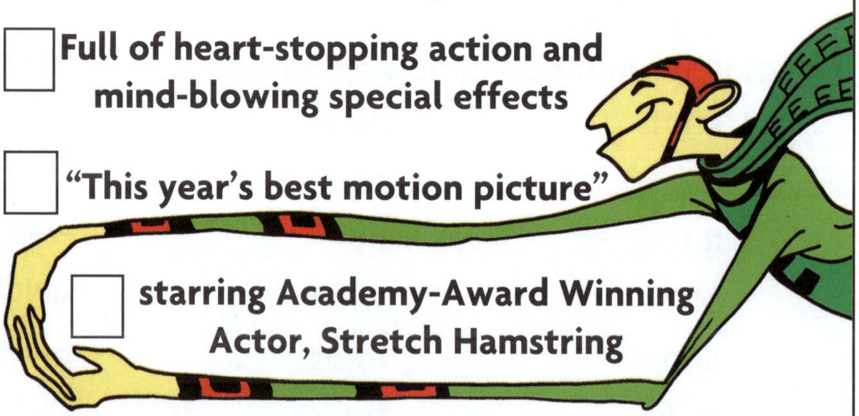

[ ] Full of heart-stopping action and mind-blowing special effects

[ ] "This year's best motion picture"

[ ] starring Academy-Award Winning Actor, Stretch Hamstring

[ ] now showing at the new Movie Town Theater

[ ] rated PG

On another sheet of paper, design an ad for the Super Squirt Water Toy. Include two facts and two opinions.

Sharks

There are over 350 different kinds of sharks. The whale shark is the largest. It is as big as a whale. The pygmy shark is the smallest. It is only about seven inches long.

All sharks live in the ocean, which is salt water, but a few kinds can swim from salt water to fresh water. Bull sharks have been found in the Mississippi River!

Sharks do not have bones. They have skeletons made of cartilage, which is the same thing your ears and nose are made of. A shark's skin is made of spiky, hard scales. The jaws of a shark are the most powerful on earth. When a great white shark bites, it clamps down on its prey and thrashes its head from side to side. It is the deadliest shark.

Sharks eat fish, dolphins and seals. The tiger shark will eat just about anything. Some fishermen have discovered unopened cans of food, clocks, boat cushions and even a keg of nails inside tiger sharks. Sometimes sharks even eat other sharks. For example, a tiger shark might eat a bull shark. The bull shark might have eaten a blacktip shark. The blacktip shark might have eaten a dogfish shark. So a tiger shark could be found with three sharks in its stomach!

Some sharks are very strange. The hammerhead shark has a head shaped somewhat like a hammer, with eyes set very far apart. A cookie cutter shark has a circular set of teeth. When it bites a dolphin or whale, it leaves a perfectly round hole in its victim. The sawshark has a snout with sharp teeth on the outside, which makes it look like a saw. The goblin shark has a sharp-pointed spear coming out of its head and its ragged teeth make it look scary!

The mako shark is the fastest swimmer. Sometimes makos have been known to leap out of the water, right into a boat! These are just a few of the many kinds of fascinating sharks.

Complete the chart with the name of the correct shark. If the statement is about all sharks, write *all*.

1. the largest shark	whale shark
2. the smallest shark	
3. the deadliest shark	
4. the fastest swimmer	
5. live in the ocean	
6. have skeletons of cartilage	
7. has a sharp-pointed spear coming out of its head	
8. has a head shaped like a hammer	
9. have skin of spiky, hard scales	
10. leaves a round bite mark	
11. looks like a saw	
12. has eaten unopened cans, clocks and boat cushions	

Read more about two different kinds of sharks. On another sheet of paper, list two similarities and two differences.

Find the Patterns

What is the pattern for the numbers 0, 2, 4, 6, 8, 10, 12, 14, 16, 18?
The pattern shows multiples of 2.

Complete each pattern.

A. **3, 6, 9, 12,** ______, ______, ______, ______, ______

B. **4, 8, 12, 16,** ______, ______, ______, ______, ______

C. **1, 2, 3, 4,** ______, ______, ______, ______, ______

D. **7, 14, 21,** ______, ______, ______, ______, ______

E. **10, 20, 30,** ______, ______, ______, ______, ______

F. ______, **18, 27,** ______, ______, ______, ______

G. **6, 12,** ______, ______, **30,** ______, ______, ______

H. ______, **22,** ______, **44,** ______, ______,**77**

I. **5, 10, 15,** ______, ______, ______, ______, ______

J. **8,** ______, **24,** ______, **40,** ______, ______, ______

K. **10, 12, 14,** ______, ______, ______, **22,** ______, ______

L. ______, **24,** ______, **48, 60,** ______, ______, ______, ______

Sam ran every afternoon last week. On Sunday, he ran 3 km. On Monday, he ran 6 km. On Wednesday, he ran 12 km. How many miles do you think he ran on Tuesday?

Moving West

Subtract. Follow the even sums to guide the settlers to their new home.

58 − 33

99 − 27

35 − 11

74 − 60

57 − 33

95 − 43

86 − 42

65 − 22

94 − 41

63 − 41

48 − 22

47 − 25

68 − 44

66 − 24

53 − 41

74 − 32

61 − 21

34 − 13

97 − 42

54 − 10

74 − 63

49 − 15

86 − 53

82 − 62

76 − 26

76 − 55

29 − 16

37 − 13

83 − 61

79 − 25

24 − 14

69 − 41

98 − 24

57 − 23

45 − 13

88 − 46

Helping Your Child Get Ready: Week 2

These are the skills your child will be working on this week.

Math
- subtracting 2-digit numbers with regrouping
- adding and subtracting money

Reading
- sequencing
- identifying story elements

Writing
- proofreading

Vocabulary
- often-confused words
- roots words

Grammar
- adjectives
- parts of speech

Here are some activities you and your child might enjoy.

Menu Planner Invite your child to plan the family's dinner menu. Be sure he or she heeds the food pyramid nutritional guidelines.

Start Collecting Having a collection is a great way for a child to develop higher-level thinking skills like sorting and analysing. Encourage your child to start one. Leaves, rocks, stamps, or shells are all easy and fun things to collect.

Invent a Board Game With a few pieces of cardboard and some coloured markers, your child can create his or her own board game. To start, suggest he or she model the game on any popular board game. The game might have a special theme, like knights or dinosaurs. Be sure he or she writes out directions for the game. Then play a round!

Flashcard Facts Have your child create his or her own set of multiplication facts flashcards. Then use them on a regular basis to help keep computation skills sharp.

Your child might enjoy reading the following books:

Pippi Longstocking
by Astrid Lindgren

Sarah, Plain and Tall
by Patricia MacLachlan

The Selfish Giant
by Oscar Wilde

____________________'s Incentive Chart: Week 2

Name Here

This week, I plan to read __________ minutes each day.

CHART YOUR PROGRESS HERE.

Week 2	Day 1	Day 2	Day 3	Day 4	Day 5
 **I read for...**	minutes	minutes	minutes	minutes	minutes
Put a sticker to show you completed each day's work.					

Congratulations!

Wow! You did a great job this week!

Place sticker here.

Parent or Caregiver's Signature ____________________________

My Crazy Dream

I don't know why, but I went to school in my underwear. Everyone was laughing! I walked up and down the hall looking for my classroom, but I could never find it. Then I went to the Lost and Found box and put on some clothes. I heard my principal say, "Son, are you lost?" However, when I turned around, it was the President of the United States talking to me. He asked me to fly on his jet with him. As we were flying, I looked out the window and saw a pterodactyl flying next to us! How could that be? They are extinct! It smiled and waved good-bye. Then all of a sudden, the airplane turned into a roller coaster. It climbed upward a million miles, then down we went! For hours and hours we just kept going straight down! The roller coaster finally came to a stop and I was on an island made entirely of chocolate. I ate a whole tree made of fudge! Then someone sneaked up behind me and captured me. He put me in a pot of boiling water to make soup out of me. I got hotter and hotter and hotter! Finally, I woke up and realised I had fallen asleep with my electric blanket on high.

Number the pictures to retell the order of what happened in the dream.

On another sheet of paper, draw a picture of a dream you once had. Then write a sentence about the beginning, middle and end of the dream on separate strips of paper. Have a family member put the sentences in order.

Attack of the Massive Melon!

Don't read this story yet! Give it to a partner and ask him or her to tell you the parts of speech under the blanks below. You give a word for each part of speech and your partner writes it in the blank. Then he or she writes the words in the story and reads the story aloud.

1. ________ ADJECTIVE ENDING IN *EST*
2. ________ NOUN
3. ________ PLURAL NOUN
4. ________ ADJECTIVE
5. ________ NOUN
6. ________ VERB ENDING IN *ING*
7. ________ FAMOUS PERSON
8. ________ ADJECTIVE
9. ________ ADVERB
10. ________ NOUN
11. ________ FAVOURITE FOOD
12. ________ NUMBER
13. ________ BODY PART
14. ________ VERB

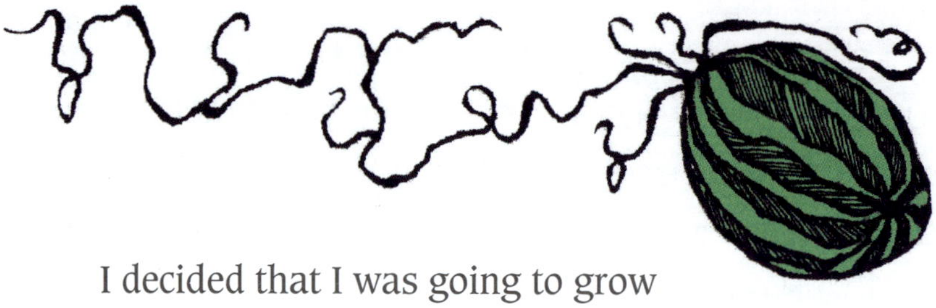

I decided that I was going to grow the ________ (1) garden in the world. I used a ________ (2) to dig holes in the backyard; then I spread seeds and ________ (3) all around. Pretty soon, my garden started looking ________ (4). I had planted ________ (5) seeds, but a watermelon started ________ (6) out of the ground! It grew and grew. This watermelon became bigger than ________ (7)! Mom said we should eat it before it turned ________ (8). So every day I climbed ________ (9) up a ________ (10), then leaped to the top of the melon and cut off huge pieces. We made watermelon shakes, peanut butter and watermelon sandwiches and ________ (11) with watermelon sauce. I've eaten almost nothing but melon for the last ________ (12) months! Mom said, "Don't look a gift horse in the ________ (13)." I sure learned a lesson: Don't bite off more than you can ________ (14)!

Accept or Except?

Some words are confusing because they are similar in some way.

Read each sentence and question. Decide which underlined word correctly answers the question. Then write the word.

1. A package just arrived for Jason. Did he accept it or did he except it? ____________	2. Sam had a sundae after dinner. Did he have desert or dessert? ____________
3. Beth made a right triangle. Does it have three angels or angles? ____________	4. All the actors sang and danced the last number. Did they perform the finale or the finally? ____________
5. Megan swam the length of the pool underwater. Did she hold her breathe or her breath? ____________	6. Aaron's socks slid down to his ankles. Were they loose or lose? ____________
7. Jerome just made a dental appointment. Should he mark it on the colander or the calendar? ____________	8. Lisa opened the gate and watched as the cows ate grass. Are the cows out to pastor or pasture? ____________
9. Meg addressed an envelope. Should she add a coma or comma between the town and state? ____________	10. Anna sketched a scene from a story she just read. Did she draw a pitcher or a picture? ____________

Are there any words that confuse you? Record them in a notebook. Include the definition and a sentence using the word. Think of ways to help yourself remember confusing words.

Great Vacations

Subtract. Draw a line from each difference to the vacation spot on the map.

Mount Rushmore	Niagara Falls	Gateway Arch	Four Corners Monument	Statue of Liberty
72 − 27	57 − 29	58 − 39	93 − 19	94 − 29

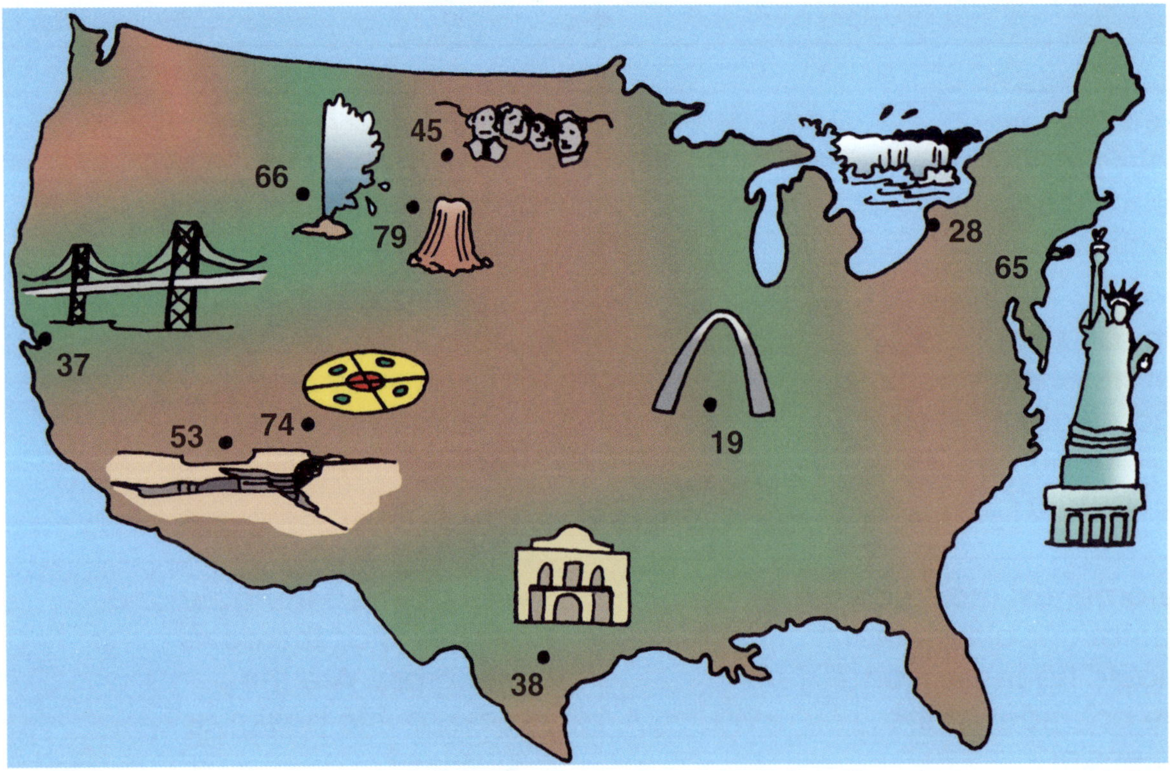

Grand Canyon	Devil's Tower	Golden Gate Bridge	The Alamo	Old Faithful
82 − 29	93 − 14	64 − 27	66 − 28	94 − 28

On the map above, mark and write the name of a vacation spot in the United States you would like to visit. Write a subtraction problem for it.

Diary of a Dog

by Louie the Dog

Find and mark the 12 errors. They may be spelling, punctuation, capitalisation, or grammar errors.

Dear Diary,

Today I get up. I did some scrathing because my neck itched. Then I slept. Then I did some sniffing around. Then I slept. Then I barked at the maillman. After that, I took a nap until dinnertime. for dinner, I had pellets in a dish. then I went back to sleep.

Yours truly, **Louie**

Dear Diary,

Today I saw a small white cats out in the yard. This really made me mad! So I barked a lot. I felt better afterwards. Do you know what I ate for dinner. I ate pellets! I washed it all down with a big slirp of water. Then I go back to sleep.

Yours truly, **Louie**

Dear Diary,

I just felt like barking todae. So I barked and barked. Then I eaten pellets and went to sleep.

Yours truly, **Louie**

Dear Diary,

That mailman comes every day. I'm getting tired of banking at him. But I did it anyway. Also, I took a walk. Tomorrow I'll catch up on my sleeping.

Yours truly, **Louie**

Did You Know?

Add or subtract. Write the letter for the matching number below to find out whose face is on the ₹500 note.

T. ₹27.99 + ₹63.84 = ____

A. ₹25.59 + ₹44.96 = ____

N. ₹71.90 − ₹59.17 = ____

M. ₹13.88 + ₹28.08 = ____

G. ₹80.31 − ₹46.16 = ____

A. ₹25.79 + ₹38.51 = ____

I. ₹53.97 − ₹29.09 = ____

H. ₹27.66 + ₹43.74 = ____

H. ₹32.48 + ₹17.77 = ____

A. ₹94.33 − ₹56.34 = ____

M. ₹13.88 + ₹18.88 = ____

A. ₹68.74 − ₹55.29 = ____

D. ₹63.89 + ₹26.53 = ____

____	____	____	____	____	____	____
₹32.76	₹70.55	₹71.40	₹64.30	₹91.83	₹41.96	₹37.99

____	____	____	____	____	____
₹34.15	₹13.45	₹12.73	₹90.42	₹50.25	₹24.88

Best Friends

Amy dreaded recess every day. She did not have any friends to play with. All the girls in her class were paired up with a best friend or in groups and she always felt left out. So, instead of playing with anyone, Amy just walked around by herself. She wanted to seesaw, but that is something you need to do with a friend. She liked to swing, but she could not go very high. She wished someone would push her to get her started.

One day, the teacher, Mrs. Gibbs, walked up and put her arm around Amy. "What's the matter, Amy? Why don't you play with the other children?" she asked.

Amy replied, "Everyone has a friend except me. I don't have anyone." Mrs. Gibbs smiled and said, "Amy, the way to get a friend is to be a friend." Amy asked, "How do I do that?"

Mrs. Gibbs answered, "Look around the playground. There are three classes of third-graders out here during this recess time. Find someone who is alone and needs a friend. Then go to that person and ask them to play." Amy said she would think about it, but she was afraid she would be too embarrassed. She wasn't sure she could do it.

The next day, Amy noticed a dark-haired girl all alone on the playground. She worked up her courage and walked over to the girl. "Hi! My name is Amy. Do you want to play with me?" she asked.

"Okay," the girl said shyly. As they took turns pushing each other on the swings, Amy found out that the girl's name was Ming. She and her family had just moved from Japan. She did not know anyone and could not speak much English yet. She needed a friend.

"Want to seesaw?" Amy asked. Ming looked puzzled. Amy pointed to the seesaw. Ming smiled and nodded. Amy was so happy. She finally had a friend!

On each blank, write the letter of the picture that correctly answers the question. One answer is used twice.

1. **Where does this story take place?** ________
2. **Who is the main character in the story?** ________

   Who are the other two characters in the story? ________ **and** ________
3. **What is the problem in the story?** ________
4. **How does Amy solve her problem?** ________
5. **What is Ming's problem?** ________

   How does Ming's problem get solved? ________

Think about what you did during breakfast or another part of your day. On another sheet of paper, list the characters, setting, problem and solution. Use this list to write a story. Read the story to a family member.

Add an Adjective

An adjective is a word that describes a noun. An adjective often tells what kind or how many.

Look at the noun, *arrow*, at the top of the triangle. Then read each line. The adjectives are underlined. Note how they help to tell more about the arrow.

Complete these triangles. Add adjectives on each line to describe the nouns.

arrow

red arrow

sleek red arrow

straight sleek red arrow

cat

__________ **cat**

__________ __________ **cat**

__________ __________ __________ **cat**

mitten

__________ **mitten**

__________ __________ **mitten**

__________ __________ __________ **mitten**

clown

__________ **clown**

__________ __________ **clown**

__________ __________ __________ **clown**

Write a sentence using the noun and all the adjectives from one of the triangles you completed.

____

____

The Root of the Matter

A word can have different parts. Many words have a main part, or **root**. *The root contains the basic meaning of the word. For example,* ped *is the root in the word* pedal. *The meaning of* ped *is "foot." Feet are used to push down on the pedals of a bicycle to cause it to move.*

The root is missing from a word in each sentence below. Use context clues and the meaning of the roots in the box to figure out the missing word part. Then write it in the space to complete the word.

pos = place	**phon** = sound	**photo** = light
port = carry	**pop** = people	

1. **The ______ulation of our town is just over 20,000.**
2. **The orchestra will perform a sym______y by Beethoven next week.**
3. **The ______ition of the hour hand shows that it is 2.00 P.M.**
4. **What goods does our country ex______ to other countries?**
5. **During ______synthesis, plants use sunlight to make food.**

List the words you completed. Then write your own definition for each word. Use a dictionary if you are not sure.

6. ____
7. ____
8. ____
9. ____
10. ____

What other words do you know with the roots ***ped, pos, phon, photo, port*** **and** ***pop?*** **On another sheet of paper, write a word containing each root. Circle the root.**

Helping Your Child Get Ready: Week 3

These are the skills your child will be working on this week.

Math
- multiplication facts
- identifying fractions
- division

Reading
- making inferences
- using context clues
- identifying overused words

Writing
- combining sentences

Vocabulary
- analogies

Grammar
- quotation marks, commas and underlining

Here are some activities you and your child might enjoy.

Idiom Illustrations Help your child develop an understanding of idioms by asking him or her to illustrate some. Some examples are "have your cake and eat it too" and "out of the frying pan and into the fire."

Compound It Ask your child to see how many compound words he or she can list that contain the word *man*.

ABC Order Read a list of eight to ten words to your child. Then have him or her put the words in alphabetical order.

Weather Watch Have your child track the weather for a week. He or she can record the temperature and precipitation each day on a chart. You might also have him or her compare the weather forecast to the actual weather.

Your child might enjoy reading the following books:

Amber Brown Is Not a Crayon
by Paula Danziger

Bone: Out From Boneville
by Jeff Smith

Superfudge
by Judy Blume

_____________________ 's Incentive Chart: Week 3

Name Here

This week, I plan to read __________ minutes each day.

CHART YOUR PROGRESS HERE.

Week 3	Day 1	Day 2	Day 3	Day 4	Day 5
 I read for...	minutes	minutes	minutes	minutes	minutes
Put a sticker to show you completed each day's work.					

Congratulations!

Wow! You did a great job this week!

Place sticker here.

Parent or Caregiver's Signature ______________________________

Multiplication Success

Why are multiplicationists so successful?

To find out, multiply. Then use the code to write the letter of each multiplication sentence on the blank above its product.

A. 10 x 10 =	G. 3 x 1 =	N. 12 x 8 =	S. 6 x 9 =
B. 6 x 7 =	H. 9 x 9 =	O. 6 x 6 =	T. 6 x 0 =
C. 5 x 6 =	I. 8 x 9 =	P. 11 x 12 =	U. 5 x 8 =
E. 7 x 7 =	L. 12 x 2 =	Q. 8 x 8 =	V. 7 x 3 =
F. 3 x 9 =	M. 3 x 6 =	R. 4 x 5 =	Y. 2 x 8 =

49 21 49 20 16   132 20 36 42 24 49 18

0 81 49 16   49 96 30 36 40 96 0 49 20

72 96   24 72 27 49

42 49 30 36 18 49 54   100

30 81 100 24 24 49 96 3 49

0 36   30 36 96 64 40 49 20 !

Order the Combination

Have you ever noticed how short sentences can make your writing sound choppy? When two sentences have different subjects and the same predicate, you can use the conjunction and *to combine them into one sentence with a compound subject.*

My friends ordered a cheese pizza. I ordered a cheese pizza.
My friends and I ordered a cheese pizza.

When two sentences have the same subject and different predicates, you can use and *to combine them into one sentence with a compound predicate.*

My mom ordered. She had pasta instead.
My mom ordered and had pasta instead.

When two sentences have the same subject and predicate and different objects, you can combine them into one sentence with a compound object using and.

My dad wanted mushrooms on his pizza. He also wanted onions.
My dad wanted mushrooms and onions on his pizza.

Fill in the missing subject, object, or predicate in each set of shorter sentences. Then combine the sentences by making compound subjects, objects, or predicates using *and*.

1. ______________________ are sweet and juicy.
   ______________________ are sweet and juicy.
   ____

2. I ______________________ about the history of basketball for homework.
   I ______________________ about the history of basketball for homework.
   ____

3. ______________________ is so much fun!
   ______________________ is also so much fun! (Change *is* to *are*.)
   ____

4. I like ______________________ more than broccoli or cauliflower.
   I like ______________________ more than broccoli or cauliflower.
   ____

5. I'd like to have ______________________ for breakfast.
   I'd also like to have ______________________ for breakfast.
   ____

Part of a Whole

Some things are parts of other things. For example, a page is a part of a book. First read each sentence. Note the underlined words. Then tell how the words in the first pair are related and how the words in the second pair are related.

Tip

A page is to a notebook as an eraser is to a pencil.

Say to yourself: A page is part of a notebook and an eraser is part of a pencil.

1. **A map is to an atlas as a definition is to a dictionary.** ____________________

____

2. **A wing is to a bird as a fin is to a fish.** ____________________

____

3. **Sand is to a beach as trees are to a forest.** ____________________

____

4. **A mattress is to a bed as a cushion is to a chair.** ____________________

____

5. **A recipe is to a cookbook as a photo is to an album.** ____________________

____

Make up a part/whole analogy for someone in your home to complete.

No Way!

To divide with remainders, follow these steps.

1. *Does 8 x __ = 34? No!*

   $8\overline{)34}$

2. *Use the closest smaller dividend.*
   8 x 4 = 32

   $$\begin{array}{r} 4 \\ 8\overline{)34} \\ 32 \end{array}$$

3. *Subtract to find the remainder.*

   $$\begin{array}{r} 4 \\ 8\overline{)34} \\ -32 \\ \hline 2 \end{array}$$

4. *The remainder is always less than the divisor.*

   $$\begin{array}{r} 4\ R2 \\ 8\overline{)34} \\ -32 \\ \hline 2 \end{array}$$

Divide. Then use the code to complete the riddle below.

E. $9\overline{)84}$	L. $3\overline{)29}$	S. $7\overline{)67}$	O. $5\overline{)24}$
T. $6\overline{)23}$	N. $6\overline{)47}$	P. $6\overline{)39}$	I. $7\overline{)52}$
O. $4\overline{)19}$	A. $8\overline{)70}$	T. $3\overline{)26}$	S. $9\overline{)55}$
H. $4\overline{)23}$	! $7\overline{)45}$	R. $5\overline{)27}$	N. $8\overline{)79}$

Emily: **Yesterday I saw a man at the mall with very long arms. Every time he went up the stairs he stepped on them.**

Jack: **Wow! He stepped on his arms?**

Emily: ____ ____, ____ ____ ____ ____ ____

7 R5 4 R4, 4 R3 9 R7 8 R2 5 R3 9 R3

____ ____ ____ ____ ____ ____ ____

9 R4 3 R5 8 R6 7 R3 5 R2 6 R1 6 R3

Monroe's Mighty Youth Tonic

Way back yonder in 1853, a traveling salesman named "Shifty" Sam Monroe rode into our little town of Dry Gulch. I was there that day when Shifty stood on the steps of his **buckboard** selling Monroe's Mighty Youth Tonic. Shifty announced, "Ladies and gentlemen, **lend me your ears**. I, Sam Monroe, have invented a tonic that will give you back your youth. It will **put a spring in your step**. You'll feel years younger if you take a spoonful of this **heavenly elixir** once a day. It contains a **special blend of secret ingredients**. Why, it once made a 94-year-old cowboy feel so young, he went back to **bustin' broncs** again! An old settler that was over 100 felt so young he let out a **war whoop** that could be heard in Pike County! **It's a steal** at only one dollar a bottle. Step right up and get yours now." Well, I wondered what those secret ingredients were, so I bought a bottle and tasted it. It tasted like nothing but sugar water. So I hid behind Shifty Sam's wagon and waited for the crowd to **mosey** on home. When Shifty went inside to make some more tonic, I **kept my eye on him**. Sure enough, he mixed sugar and water and added a drop of vanilla. We'd been **hornswoggled**! I **hightailed it** right then over to the sheriff's office and had him arrest that no-good varmint. Old Shifty is now spending the rest of his "mighty youth" **behind bars**!

Howdy, partner! Read the bold words in the story on page 51. What do they mean? Hitch up the words on the left with the correct meanings on the right.

1. **way back yonder**
2. **buckboard**
3. **Lend me your ears.**
4. **Put a spring in your step.**
5. **heavenly elixir**
6. **special blend of secret ingredients**
7. **bustin' broncs**
8. **war whoop**
9. **It's a steal!**
10. **mosey**
11. **kept my eye on him**
12. **hornswoggled**
13. **hightailed it**
14. **no-good varmint**
15. **behind bars**

walk slowly

cheated; tricked

watched him closely

making wild horses gentle

ran quickly

troublesome creature

Listen to me.

in jail

wagon

You are getting it for a low price.

I won't tell what's in it.

makes you feel peppy

many years ago

loud yell

wonderful tonic

Where Am I?

Making inferences *means to use information in a story to make judgments about information not given in the story.*

Read each riddle below. Look for clues to help you answer each question.

1. It is dark in here. I hear bats flying. With my flashlight, I see stalactites hanging above me. I hear water dripping. Where am I?

   ____

2. Let's sit in the front row! Ha ha ha! That's funny . . . a cartoon about a drink cup that is singing to a candy bar. That makes me hungry. I think I'll go get some popcorn before it starts. Where am I?

   ____

3. This thing keeps going faster and faster, up and down and over and around. It tickles my tummy. The girls behind me are screaming. I hope I don't go flying out of my seat! Where am I?

   ____

4. I can see rivers and highways that look like tiny ribbons. I am glad I got to sit by the window. Wow, we are in a cloud! Yes, ma'am. I would like a snack. Thank you. Where am I?

   ____

5. I am all dressed up, sitting here quietly with my parents. The flowers are pretty. The music is starting. Here she comes down the aisle. I wish they would hurry so I can have some cake! Where am I?

   ____

6. Doctor, can you help my dog? His name is Champ. He was bitten by a snake and his leg is swollen. I hope he will be all right. Where am I?

   ____

7. How will I ever decide? Look at all the different kinds. There are red hots, chocolates, candy corn, gummy worms, jawbreakers and lollipops. Boy, this is my favourite place in the mall! Where am I?

   ____

8. This row has carrots growing and this one has onions. The corn is getting tall. The soil feels dry. I better water the plants today. Don't you think so, Mr. Scarecrow? Where am I?

   ____

On another sheet of paper, write two "Where Am I?" riddles of your own. Read your riddles to someone else and have them guess where you are.

Using Punctuation

Quotation marks show the exact words of a speaker. **Commas** appear between the day and year in a date, between the city and state in a location, between the lines of an address and after all but the last item in a series. **Underlining** shows book titles.

A. **Read each sentence. Add any missing commas.**

1. Mrs Wu's bank is located at 18-20 MG Road Fort Mumbai 400001.
2. She opened an account there on September 8 2001.
3. She also uses the branch office in Bandra (West.
4. That branch is open weekdays Saturdays and some evenings.
5. The main office is closed Saturdays Sundays and all holidays.
6. Mrs Wu saw Ms Ames Mr Pacheco and Mrs Jefferson at the bank on Saturday.
7. They carried checks bills and deposits.
8. Mr Pacheco has had an account at that bank since May 2 1974.

B. **Read the sentences below. Add any missing quotation marks, commas, or underlining.**

1. My favourite author is Ruskin Bond said Rick.
2. Bond was born on May 19, 1934.
3. He lives in Landour Mussoorie.
4. What are your favourite books by him? asked Teresa.
5. I like The Room On the Roof and The Blue Umbrella replied Rick.

Write a sentence that tells your own mailing address. Then name three things you enjoy receiving in the mail, such as letters from friends, magazines, or catalogs.

Numerous, Spectacular Words

When you write, do you sometimes overuse descriptive words like good, bad, nice, *or* wonderful? *Overused words can make your writing boring.*

The weather was **good** *for our first camping trip. (fair)*
A ranger gave us some really **good** *tips about the park. (useful)*
Mom thought the campsite near the stream was **good**. *(lovely)*
My older brother is a **good** *fly fisherman. (skilled)*
He said his equipment is too **good** *for me to use, though! (valuable)*

Now reread the sentences. This time use the words in parentheses in place of the word good. *You can use a thesaurus to help find words. A thesaurus is a reference tool that gives synonyms and antonyms for words.*

Identify eight frequently overused descriptive words in the passage below and list them in the answer spaces. Next, use a thesaurus to write three synonyms for each word, or write three synonyms you know. Then revise the passage. Use editing symbols to cross out the overused words and add the more effective synonyms to replace them.

Our family has a dog named Scooter. He's normally good until it's time to bathe him. That's when our nice, little terrier turns into a big, furry monster. Scooter isn't really bad. He's just hard to handle when he doesn't want to do something. I think he's afraid of water. You should see how sad he looks once we manage to get him into the tub.

1. ____________________ ____
2. ____________________ ____
3. ____________________ ____
4. ____________________ ____
5. ____________________ ____
6. ____________________ ____
7. ____________________ ____
8. ____________________ ____

Reread a composition you wrote last year. Look for overused words and then use a thesaurus to find other words that you could use instead to make your writing more interesting.

What Is a Fraction?

A fraction consists of two parts.

$\frac{3}{4}$ *The* **numerator** *tells how many parts are being identified.*
The **denominator** *tells the total number of equal parts in the whole.*

Write the name of each fraction.

A. 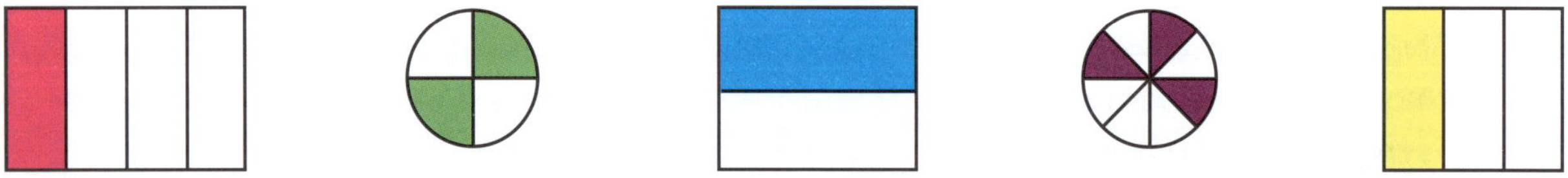

B. 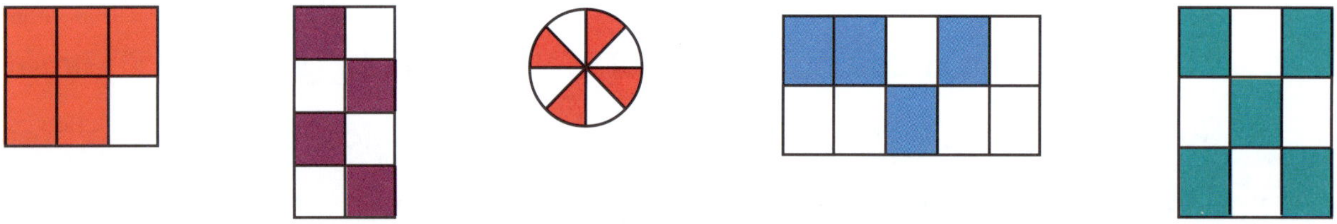

C. 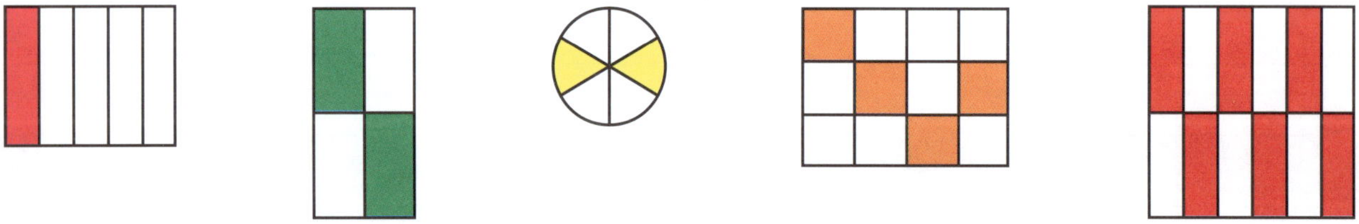

Helping Your Child Get Ready: Week 4

These are the skills your child will be working on this week.

Math
- multiplication facts
- 2-digit multiplication; logic

Reading
- finding the main idea
- comparing and contrasting

Writing
- using similes and metaphors
- expanding sentences

Vocabulary
- idioms

Grammar
- verb tenses
- contractions

Here are some activities you and your child might enjoy.

Homograph Duos Ask your child to use each of the homographs *pen*, *uniform* and *base* in two sentences that each show one of the word's meanings. For example, *Joe's pen was out of ink* and *The pigs ran out of the pen.*

What's Your Estimate Ask your child to estimate how many times in 60 seconds he or she can . . .

a) say "Maharashtra" **b)** touch his or her toes

Then have him or her try each activity and compare the results with the estimate.

Order, Please! Have your child put these time-period words in order from shortest to longest.

hour	week	millisecond
decade	day	minute

Tongue Twisters Have fun with tongue twisters. See how many times your child can say a tongue twister in one minute. Here are some examples to get you started: "Some shun sunshine" and "How much wood would a wood chuck chuck if a wood chuck could chuck wood?"

Your child might enjoy reading the following books:

Monster Slick and the Magic Umbrella
by Sanket Pethkar

I'm a Real Boy
by Clayton Koh

The Meanwhile Adventures (Roddy Doyle)
by Roddy Doyle

______________________ **'s Incentive Chart: Week 4**

Name Here

This week, I plan to read ____________ minutes each day.

CHART YOUR PROGRESS HERE.

Week 4	Day 1	Day 2	Day 3	Day 4	Day 5
 I read for...	minutes	minutes	minutes	minutes	minutes
Put a sticker to show you completed each day's work.					

Congratulations!

Wow! You did a great job this week!

Place sticker here.

Parent or Caregiver's Signature ______________________________

Colourful Clues

You can compare two things that are not alike in order to give your readers a clearer and more colourful picture. When you use like *or* as *to make a comparison, it is called a* **simile***.*

Max is as slow as molasses when he doesn't want to do something.
My sister leaped over the puddles like a frog to avoid getting her shoes wet.
The angry man erupted like a volcano.

When you make a comparison without like *or* as*, it is called a* **metaphor***.*
You compare things directly, saying the subject is something else.

The disturbed anthill was a whirlwind of activity.
The oak trees, silent sentries around the cabin, stood guard.
Jenny and I were all ears as we listened to the latest gossip.

Finish the metaphors and similes.

1. **Crowds of commuters piled into the subway cars like** ____________________
____
2. **Chirping crickets on warm summer night are** ____________________
____
3. **After rolling in the mud, our dog looked like** ____________________
4. **Happiness is** ____________________
5. **Just learning to walk, the toddler was as wobbly as** ____________________
____
6. **After scoring the winning point, I felt as** ____________________
____
7. **Having a tooth filled is about as much fun as** ____________________
____
8. **A summer thunderstorm is** ____________________
____
9. ____________________ **is** ____________________
10. ____________________ **is like** ____________________

Piece of Cake!

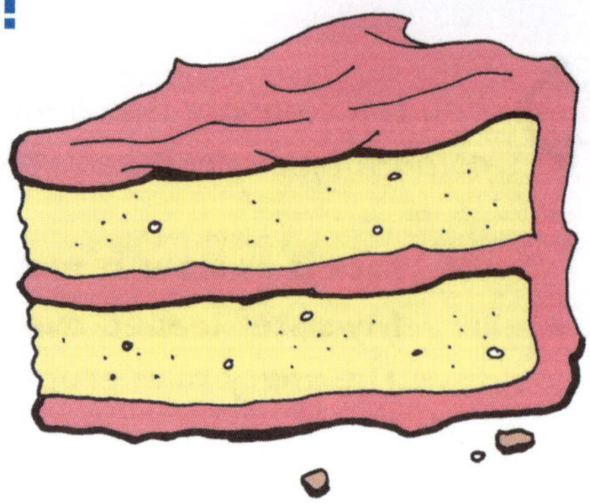

Piece of cake *is an example of a common* **idiom**, *or expression. It means "an easy task." It is difficult to understand the meaning of the idiom by using the ordinary meaning of the words.*

What does the idiom in each sentence mean? Circle the letter of the meaning that makes the most sense.

1. Jason was so tired that he *hit the hay* right after dinner.
   a. went to bed **b.** went back to work **c.** cut the grass
2. Do not waste your money on this video because it is *for the birds.*
   a. worthless **b.** fantastic **c.** expensive
3. Jasmine was *down in the dumps* after losing the game.
   a. smelly **b.** excited **c.** sad
4. "Rap music is definitely *not my cup of tea,*" said Jack's grandmother.
   a. not cheap **b.** not to my liking **c.** not hot enough
5. Ben and Lisa do not *see eye to eye* about which movie to watch.
   a. agree **b.** disagree **c.** argue
6. "I don't recall his name," said Kim, "but his face *rings a bell.*"
   a. is unfamiliar **b.** stirs a memory **c.** appears
7. Carlos has been *on cloud nine* since winning the contest.
   a. very unhappy **b.** unfriendly **c.** joyous
8. The two old men were sitting on the park bench *chewing the fat.*
   a. feeding the squirrels **b.** having a friendly chat **c.** eating lunch
9. Although he was losing by 20 points, Alex refused to *throw in the towel.*
   a. give up **b.** take a shower **c.** do laundry
10. I *kept a straight face* when I saw Ann's wild new hairdo.
    a. poked fun **b.** kept from laughing **c.** stared

Listen for idioms in conversations you hear throughout the day. Write them down in a notebook. If you do not know what an idiom means, try to find out.

Maze

Trace a path to Ocean Beach through seven correctly spelled contractions. You cannot pass through any areas with misspelled contractions; they act like blocks and force you to go back and try a different route.

What a Nose!

An elephant's trunk is probably the most useful nose in the world. Of course, it is used for breathing and smelling, like most noses are. However, elephants also use their trunks like arms and hands to lift food to their mouths. They suck water into their trunks and pour it into their mouths to get a drink. Sometimes they spray the water on their backs to give themselves a cool shower. An adult elephant can hold up to four gallons of water in its trunk. Elephants can use their trunks to carry heavy things, such as logs that weigh up to 600 pounds! The tip of the trunk has a little knob on it that the elephant uses like a thumb. An elephant can use the "thumb" to pick up something as small as a coin. Trunks are also used for communication. Two elephants that meet each other touch their trunks to each other's mouth, kind of like a kiss. Sometimes a mother elephant will calm her baby by stroking it with her trunk. Can your nose do all those things?

Find the statement below that is the main idea of the story. Write *M.I.* in the elephant next to it. Then find the details of the story. Write *D* in the elephant next to each detail. Be careful! There are two sentences that do not belong in this story.

Elephants use their trunks to greet each other, like giving a kiss.

Elephants use their trunks to give themselves a shower.

Some people like to ride on elephants.

Elephants can carry heavy things with their trunks.

Mother elephants calm their babies by stroking them with their trunks.

Elephants use their trunks to eat and drink.

Elephants use their noses for smelling and breathing.

Elephants have very useful noses.

Giraffes are the tallest animals in the world.

On another sheet of paper, finish this story: *When I was on safari, I looked up and saw a herd of elephants.* **Underline the main idea.**

Stretching Sentences

A sentence is more interesting when it includes more than just a subject and a verb. It may tell where or when the sentence is happening. It may also tell why something is happening.

Write a sentence describing each set of pictures. Include a part that tells where, why or how something is happening.

1. ______________________________

2. ______________________________

3. ______________________________

4. ______________________________

Find a cartoon in the newspaper. Use the pictures to write a sentence on another sheet of paper that includes a subject, a verb and a part that tells where, when, or why.

Geometric Multiplication

Multiply. Colour each triangle with an even product orange. Colour each triangle with an odd product blue.

8 x 6 = ____	9 x 4 = ____	8 x 9 = ____	8 x 12 = ____
7 x 9 = ____	7 x 7 = ____	9 x 3 = ____	9 x 11 = ____
7 x 7 = ____	4 x 6 = ____	8 x 7 = ____	1 x 7 = ____
8 x 8 = ____	9 x 5 = ____	5 x 7 = ____	8 x 10 = ____
6 x 9 = ____	9 x 9 = ____	7 x 3 = ____	6 x 6 = ____
7 x 11 = ____	5 x 8 = ____	6 x 3 = ____	9 x 7 = ____
1 x 9 = ____	5 x 9 = ____	7 x 5 = ____	3 x 9 = ____
7 x 10 = ____	7 x 6 = ____	9 x 8 = ____	6 x 12 = ____

Maria was decorating a picture frame for her friend's birthday. She chose seven different-sized, diamond-shaped tiles to glue around the frame. There was enough room to glue four colours of each size of tile. How many tiles did she use altogether to decorate the frame? On another sheet of paper, solve this problem and draw a picture of what the frame might look like.

Special Charts

Comparing *and* **contrasting** *means to show the similarities and differences of things. A Venn diagram is a chart made of overlapping circles that can be used to organise the similarities and differences. The overlapping parts of the circles show how things are similar. The other part of the circles show how things are different.*

Joe, Kim and Rob each got a lunch tray, went through the lunch line and sat together to eat. These students all had the same lunch menu, but each one only ate what he or she liked. Joe ate chicken nuggets, green beans, applesauce and carrots. Rob ate chicken nuggets, green beans, a roll and corn. Kim ate chicken nuggets, a roll, sandwich and salad.

Today's Menu

Chicken nuggets
Corn
Green beans
Carrots
Salad
Roll
Sandwich

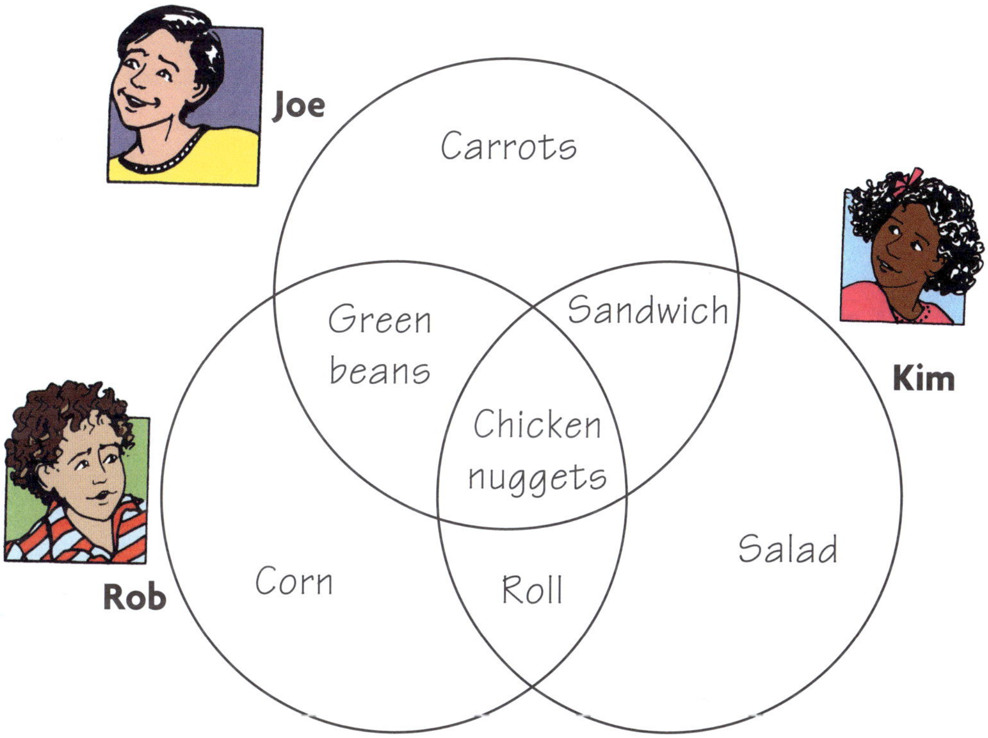

1. **What food did all three students eat?** ____________________
2. **What did Joe and Rob eat that Kim did not?** ____________________
3. **What did Joe and Kim eat that Rob did not?** ____________________
4. **What did Kim and Rob eat that Joe did not?** ____________________
5. **What did Joe eat that no one else ate?** ____________________
6. **What did Rob eat that no one else ate?** ____________________
7. **What did Kim eat that no one else ate?** ____________________

Present- and Past-Tense Verbs

Present-tense verbs show action that is happening now. They agree in number with who or what is doing the action. **Past-tense verbs** show action that took place in the past. Most past-tense verbs end in *-ed*.

A. **Read each sentence. If the underlined verb is in the present tense, write *present* on the line. If it is in the past tense, write *past*.**

1. We worked together on a jigsaw puzzle. ____________
2. Mom helped us. ____________
3. She enjoys puzzles, too. ____________
4. Tom picked out the border pieces. ____________
5. He dropped a puzzle piece on the floor. ____________
6. I looked for the flower pieces. ____________
7. Dad likes crossword puzzles better. ____________
8. My little sister watches us. ____________
9. Mom hurries us before dinner. ____________
10. We rushed to finish quickly. ____________

B. **Underline the verb in each sentence. Then rewrite the sentence. Change the present-tense verb to the past. Change the past-tense verb to the present.**

1. The man crosses the river.

____

2. He rowed his boat.

____

In the Wink of an Eye

Solve the problems. If the answer is even, connect the dot beside each problem to the heart on the right- and left-hand sides of the circle. If the answer is odd, do nothing. Two lines have been drawn for you.

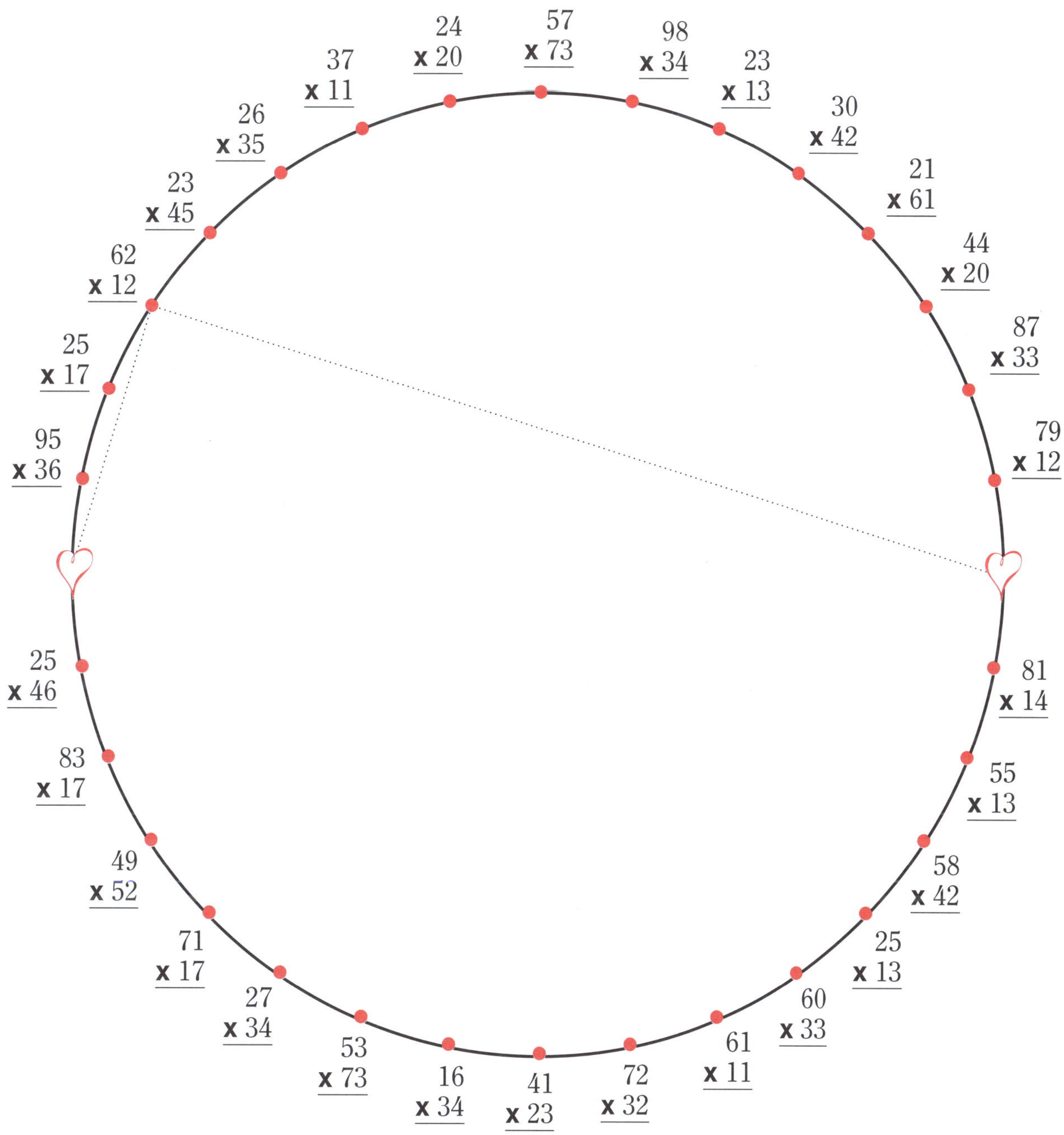

Swimming in Logic

Logic clues put the final finish on our swimcolourming competition. Read the clues and place these swimmers in the correct finishing order.

Dive Into These Clues!

1. Asher finished before Grace but after Emily.
2. Grace finished after Alicia but before Finn and Dillon.
3. Alicia finished before Emily.
4. Finn came in last.

Results:

1st ______________________

2nd ______________________

3rd ______________________

4th ______________________

5th ______________________

6th ______________________

Helping Your Child Get Ready: Week 5

These are the skills your child will be working on this week.

Math
- division with remainders
- money

Refading
- visualising
- drawing conclusions

Writing
- expanding sentences
- combining sentences

Vocabulary
- antonyms

Grammar
- capitalisation
- statements and questions

Here are some activities you and your child might enjoy.

Quick Look Ask your child to look around your kitchen and find 10 or more items that begin with the letter *S*.

Listen Up Help your child develop good listening and memorisation skills. Read the names of the first five Indian Presidents (listed here) two times.
Then ask your child to repeat the list back to you in order.

Jawaharlal Nehru, Gulzarilal Nanda, Lal Bahadur Shastri, Indira Gandhi, Morarjee Desai

Birthday Futures Have your child figure out what day of the week his or her birthday will fall on this year, next year and the year after that. Ask him or her to describe any pattern he or she notices.

Vegetable Know-How The vegetables we eat come from different parts of plants. Ask your child to keep track of the vegetables you eat for dinner for one week. Then have him or her create a chart to show which part of the plant each vegetable comes from.

Your child might enjoy reading the following books:

Book Uncle and Me
by Uma Krishnaswami

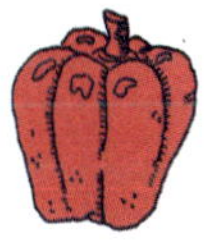

Moin and the Monster
by Anushka Ravishankar

Ramona Quimby, Age 8
by Beverly Cleary

_______________ 's Incentive Chart: Week 5

Name Here

This week, I plan to read __________ minutes each day.

CHART YOUR PROGRESS HERE.

Week 5	Day 1	Day 2	Day 3	Day 4	Day 5
 **I read for...**	minutes	minutes	minutes	minutes	minutes
Put a sticker to show you completed each day's work.					

Congratulations!

Wow! You did a great job this week!

Place sticker here.

Parent or Caregiver's Signature ____________________

Grammar Cop

and the case of the missing capital letters

The person who wrote this letter didn't really understand the laws of capital letters. Can you help Grammar Cop find the mistakes?

Circle the letters that should have been capitalized.
Hint: There are 19 mistakes.

Dear cinderella and Prince Charming,

there must be a terrible mistake! the stepsisters and I have not yet received an invitation to your wedding. i keep telling the stepsisters that the invitation will arrive soon. i'm getting worried that our invitation got lost. i hear you often have problems with the unicorns that deliver the palace mail.

I'm sure you intend to invite us! After all, you were always my special favourite. How i spoiled you! i let you do all the best chores around the house. are you still mad about that trip to disney world? i don't know how we could have forgotten you! anyway, florida is too hot in the summer.

so cinderella, dear, please send along another invitation as soon as you can. i know how busy you are in your new palace. if you need any cleaning help, i can send one of your stepsisters along. they both miss you so much!

Best wishes,
Your not really so wicked stepmother

Remember these basic laws of capital letters:

- **Names**
  Always capitalise someone's proper name. (Example: **G**ina, **K**enneth, **T**yrone)
- **Places**
  Always capitalise the name of the town, city, state and country. (Example: I live in **O**rchard **B**each, **C**alifornia, which is in the **U**nited **S**tates.)
- ***I***
  Always capitalise the letter *I* when it stands for a person. (Example: **I** am in fourth grade and **I**'m ten years old.)
- **First letter**
  Always capitalise the first letter of the first word of a sentence.

Division Decoder

Riddle: What kind of tools do you use for maths?

Find each quotient. Then use the Decoder to solve the riddle by filling in the spaces at the bottom of the page.

1. $8 \div 2$ = ________
2. $10 \div 5$ = ________
3. $24 \div 4$ = ________
4. $50 \div 10$ = ________
5. $72 \div 9$ = ________
6. $32 \div 10$ = ________
7. $48 \div 7$ = ________
8. $29 \div 3$ = ________
9. $65 \div 8$ = ________
10. $92 \div 6$ = ________

Decoder

8	I
3 remainder 2	L
7	W
8 remainder 1	S
6	U
9	A
15 remainder 3	B
4	L
2 remainder 3.	D
9 remainder 2.	T
1	F
7 remainder 6.	N
6 remainder 6..	I
2	E
11	O
15 remainder 2	P
2 remainder 5.	X
10	C
5	R

"M ___ ___ ___ ___" ___ ___ ___ ___ ___ ___

3 1 8 5 10 6 7 2 4 9

On the Contrary

***Antonyms** are words that have opposite or nearly opposite meanings. A **suffix** is added to the end of a word to change its meaning. The suffix -*ous *means "having" or "full of."*

Write a word from the box that is the antonym of the clue word to complete the crossword puzzle.

tiny	silly	unclear	unknown	stingy	tasteless
calm	few	rude	careless	safe	timid

Across
1. delicious
4. anxious
5. numerous
6. courteous
10. enormous
11. cautious

Down
1. courageous
2. dangerous
3. generous
7. famous
8. serious
9. obvious

What other words do you know that end with *-ous*? On another sheet of paper, make a list of five words. Write your own definition for each word.

Statements and Questions

A **statement** begins with a capital letter and ends with a period. A **question** begins with a capital letter and ends with a question mark.

A. **Rewrite each sentence correctly. Begin each sentence with a capital letter. Use periods and question marks correctly.**

1. can we take a taxi downtown

___

2. where does the bus go

___

3. the people on the bus waved to us

___

4. we got on the elevator

___

5. should I push the elevator button

___

B. **Write a question. Then write an answer that is a statement.**

1. Question: ___

___

2. Statement: ___

___

Stretch It!

A sentence includes a subject and a verb. A sentence is more interesting when it also includes a part that tells where, when, or why.

Add more information to each sentence by telling where, when, or why. Write the complete new sentence.

1. **Mom is taking us shopping.** Where?

____

2. **The stores are closing.** When?

____

3. **We need to find a gift for Dad.** Why?

____

4. **I will buy new jeans.** Where?

____

5. **We may eat lunch.** When?

____

Find two sentences in your favourite book that include a subject, verb and a part that tells where, when, or why. Write the sentences on another sheet of paper.

Let's Eat Out!

Two sentences can be combined to make one sentence by using the words **although**, **after**, **because**, **until** *and* **while**.

Choose a word from the menu to combine the two sentences into one sentence.

1. We are eating out tonight. Mom worked late.

____

2. We are going to Joe's Fish Shack. I do not like fish.

____

3. Dad said I can play outside. It's time to leave.

____

4. We can play video games. We are waiting for our food.

____

5. We may stop by Ida's Ice Cream Shop. We leave the restaurant.

____

Read the back of a cereal box. Find two sentences that could be combined.

The Lake Cabin

As you read the paragraph, imagine the scene that the words are describing. In the picture below, draw everything that has been left out. Colour the picture.

My favourite thing to do in the summer is to go to Grandpa's lake cabin. In the evening after a full day of fishing, Grandpa and I sit on the back porch and enjoy the scenery. The sun setting behind the mountain fills the blue sky with streaks of orange and yellow. Colourful sailboats float by us in slow motion. Suddenly a fish jumps out of the water, making tiny waves in rings. A deer quietly walks to the edge of the water to get a drink. Red and yellow wildflowers grow near the big rock. On the shore across the lake, we see a couple of tents. Someone must be camping there. A flock of geese fly over the lake in the shape of a V. Every time we sit and look at the lake, Grandpa says, "This is the best place on earth!"

On another sheet of paper, write a paragraph describing the place that you think is "the best place on earth." Read your paragraph to someone in your family.

Put the Brakes on Math Mistakes!

Take a look at the signs on Bob's store. Circle any mistakes you see. Then fix the mistakes so that the signs are correct.

Where Is Holly?

Drawing conclusions *means to make reasonable conclusions about events in a story using the information given.*

One day, while Mom was washing dishes in the kitchen, she realised that she had not heard a peep out of three-year-old Holly in a long time. The last time she had seen her, she was playing in the living room with some building blocks. "She sure is being good," thought Mom.

Write an *X* next to the best answer.

1. **Why did Mom think Holly was being good?**

   _______ **Holly was washing dishes for her.**

   _______ **Holly was playing with dolls.**

   _______ **Holly was being so quiet.**

After rinsing the last dish, Mom went to the living room to see what Holly had built. But Holly was not there. "Holly! Where are you?" Mom asked. Mom heard a faraway voice say, "Mommy!" So Mom went outside to see if Holly was there.

2. **Why did Mom go outside to look for Holly?**

   _______ **Holly's voice sounded so far away.**

   _______ **The last time Mom saw Holly, she was riding her tricycle.**

   _______ **Holly said, "I'm outside, Mommy."**

Mom looked down the street, up in the tree and in the backyard, but Holly was not outside. She called her again but did not hear her voice. So, she went back inside. "Holly! Where are you? Come out right now."

3. **Why did Mom say, "Come out right now."**

   _______ **She was mean.**

   _______ **She heard Holly's voice coming from the closet.**

   _______ **She thought Holly might be hiding.**

Once again, Mom heard a faraway sound. "Help me!" cried Holly. Mom ran to the bathroom, but Holly was not there. She ran to the garage, but Holly was not there either. Finally, she ran to Holly's room and saw Holly's feet sticking out of the toy box, kicking wildly in the air!

4. **What had happened to Holly?**

   _______ **She had fallen headfirst into the toy box and could not get out.**

   _______ **She was playing with the blocks again.**

   _______ **She was playing hide-and-seek with Mom.**

Mom lifted Holly out of the toy box and asked, "Holly, are you all right?" Holly replied, "I think so." Holly then told Mom that she had been looking for her toy piano because she wanted to play a song for her. "Do you want to hear the song now?" Holly asked. "First, let's have a special snack. You can play the piano for me later," Mom suggested. Holly thought that was a great idea!

5. **Where was Holly's toy piano?**

   _______ **The piano was under Holly's bed.**

   _______ **The piano was at the bottom of the toy box.**

   _______ **She was playing hide-and-seek with Mom.**

Mom and Holly walked to the kitchen. Mom made Holly a bowl of ice cream with chocolate sauce and a cherry on top. Holly told Mom that she wanted to go to the park. Mom really liked that idea.

6. **What will Mom and Holly do next?**

   _______ **Mom and Holly will go shopping.**

   _______ **Mom and Holly will go for a bike ride.**

   _______ **Mom and Holly will play on the swings in the park.**

Helping Your Child Get Ready: Week 6

These are the skills your child will be working on this week.

Math

- reading a table
- word problems
- 2- and 3-digit multiplication
- division
- equivalent fractions

Reading

- reading for details
- identifying story elements

Writing

- sentence elaboration

Vocabulary

- synonyms, antonyms and homophones

Grammar

- parts of speech

Here are some activities you and your child might enjoy.

Mum's the Word This is a fun dinnertime family game. Agree on a small word that is used frequently in conversation, such as *the* or *and*. This word becomes "mum." No one can say it! Anyone who does, drops out. The last person left is the winner.

Palindrome Collection Palindromes are words that are spelled the same backward and forward. Start a palindrome collection with your child. Here are some to get you going: *bob*, *toot*, *Anna* and *refer*.

One-Minute Categories Ask your child to name as many examples as possible of a particular category in one minute. For example, for animals, he or she might name dog, cat, zebra, horse and so on. Make the categories more challenging as his or her skill increases.

What's the Math Question? Ask your child to make up a question or problem to go with an answer. For example, if you say the answer is "48," he or she could say the question is "What is 12 x 4?" or "What is 54 – 6?"

Your child might enjoy reading the following books:

School Stories
by Paro Anand

Liar, Liar, Pants on Fire
by Gordon Korman

Diary of a Wimpy Kid
by Jeff Kinney

_______________ 's Incentive Chart: Week 6

Name Here

This week, I plan to read __________ minutes each day.

CHART YOUR PROGRESS HERE.

Week 6	Day 1	Day 2	Day 3	Day 4	Day 5
 I read for...	minutes	minutes	minutes	minutes	minutes
Put a sticker to show you completed each day's work.					

Congratulations!

Wow! You did a great job this week!

Place sticker here.

Parent or Caregiver's Signature ______________________________

A Perfect Match?

Each word in column 1 has a match in column 2. The match in column 2 is either a synonym (means the same thing, such as *right* and *correct*), antonym (means the opposite, such as *right* and *wrong*), or homophone (sounds the same, such as *one* and *won*). Draw a line between each match and write which type of match it is. There is only one correct match for each word.

Column 1	Column 2	Type of Match
1. modern	a. where	1. ______
2. sail	b. dusk	2. ______
3. thaw	c. gargantuan	3. ______
4. tired	d. late	4. ______
5. blue	e. sale	5. ______
6. dawn	f. ancient	6. ______
7. right	g. exhausted	7. ______
8. miniscule	h. blew	8. ______
9. wear	j. correct	9. ______
10. tardy	k. freeze	10. ______
11. grate	l. kernel	11. ______
12. assemble	m. live	12. ______
13. danger	n. hazard	13. ______
14. dwell	o. dismantle	14. ______
15. colonel	p. great	15. ______

YOUR TURN

Make a puzzle of your own like the one above. Use synonyms, antonyms and homophones. Then have someone in your family figure out what the matches are.

At the Beach

A **describing word** *makes a sentence more interesting.*

Read the describing words found in the beach balls. Add the describing words to make each sentence more interesting. Write each new sentence.

1. **The snow cone sat in the sun.**

____

2. **Many children ran toward the ocean waves.**

____

3. **My friends built a sandcastle.**

____

4. **My brother grabbed his beach toys.**

____

5. **Our dog tried to catch beach balls.**

____

On another sheet of paper, draw a beach ball. Fill it with words that describe a day at the beach.

Flying Carpet

Solve the problems. If the answer is between 100 and 250, colour the shape yellow. If the answer is between 251 and 900, colour the shape blue. Finish the design by colouring the other shapes with the colours of your choice.

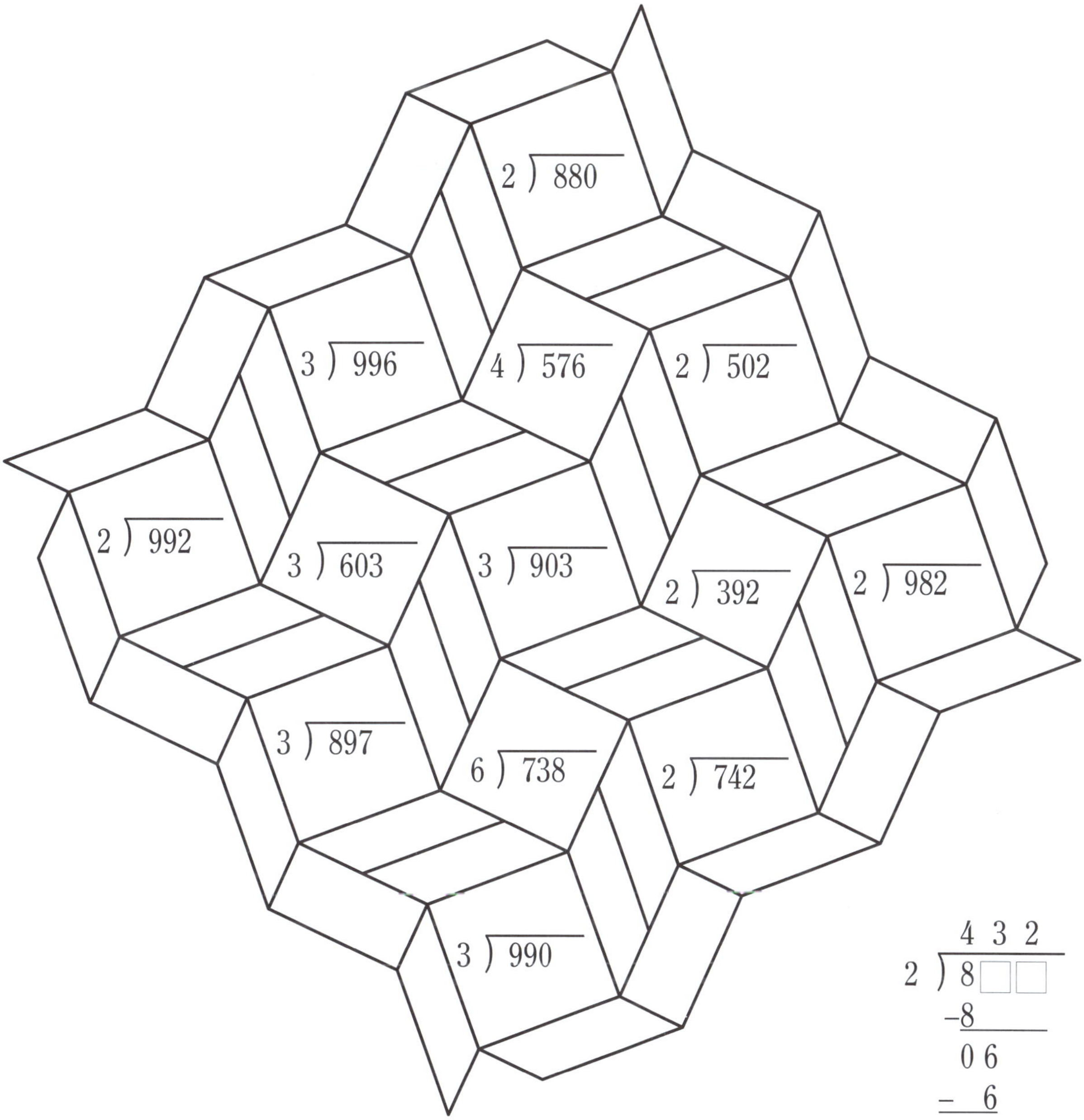

Taking It Further: Fill in the missing digits in the problem to the right.

```
      4 3 2
  2 ) 8 □ □
     -8
      0 6
     -  6
        0 4
     -    4
          0
```

Super Silly Circus

Don't read this story yet! Give it to a member of your family and ask him or her to tell you the parts of speech under the blanks below. You give a word for each part of speech and your partner writes it in the blank. Then he or she writes the words in the story and reads the story aloud.

1. ____________ YOUR CITY
2. ____________ ADJECTIVE
3. ____________ YOUR LAST NAME
4. ____________ NOUN
5. ____________ ADJECTIVE
6. ____________ VERB + *ER*
7. ____________ ADVERB
8. ____________ VERB
9. ____________ NUMBER
10. ____________ PLURAL NOUN
11. ____________ NOUN
12. ____________ BODY PART
13. ____________ PLURAL NOUN
14. ____________ ADJECTIVE
15. ____________ ADJECTIVE ENDING IN *EST*

Over the summer, the circus came to ____________ (1). Not just any ____________ (2) circus, it was the Ringling Brothers and Barnum and ____________ (3) Circus! My favourite performer was the ____________ (4) tamer who was fearless and ____________ (5). The tightrope ____________ (6) teetered ____________ (7) above the stage, looking like she was about to ____________ (8). We saw a ____________ (9)-foot-tall man juggling ____________ (10) while wearing a ____________ (11) on his ____________ (12). All day we ate ____________ (13), peanuts and popcorn until we felt ____________ (14). It really was the ____________ (15) show on earth!

Weatherman

Figure It Out!

1. Showers on Monday morning produced 0.5 inches of rain by noon. By 6 p.m., a total of 2 inches of rain had fallen. How many inches of rain fell between noon and 6 p.m.? ______________

2. On Tuesday, 1.2 inches of rain fell. Two more inches of rain fell the next day. How many inches of rain fell on Wednesday? ____________________

3. The graph shows the high temperatures for Wednesday through Sunday. On which day was the highest temperature reached? The lowest? What was the difference between the two temperatures? ____

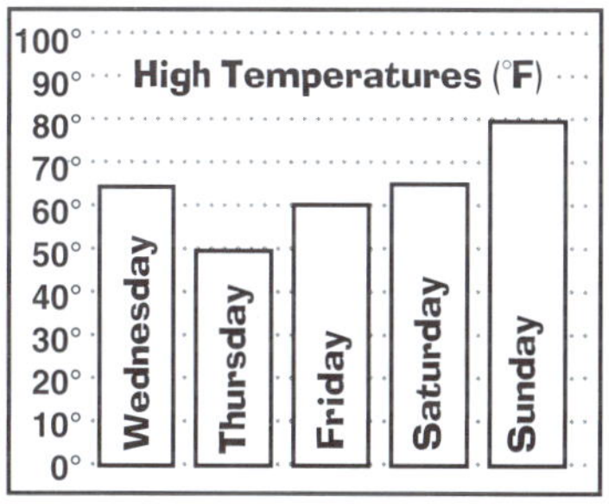

4. Between which two days did the temperature drop 15 degrees? Increase by 15 degrees? ___________________________

5. Saturday's low temperature was 38°. How many degrees did the temperature rise to reach Saturday's high temperature? ________________

SUPER CHALLENGE: What was the average high temperature for all five days shown on the graph?

Week 6 • Day 3
Reading a Table

Dining with Dinosaurs

This "Dino" table provides specific information about different kinds of dinosaurs. Use the table to choose the best answer to each question below.

DINOSAUR FACTS				
Name	**What It Means**	**Size**	**Weight**	**Food**
Ankylosaurus	Crooked lizard	25 feet	3,000 kg	plants
Baryonyx	Heavy claw	30 feet	1,500 kg	fish
Eoraptor	Dawn thief	3 feet	5-7 kg	meat, insects
Maiasaura	Good mother lizard	30 feet	3,000 kg	plants
Plateosaurus	Broad lizard	20–26 feet	900–1,800 kg	plants
Seismosaurus	Earthquake lizard	120–150 feet	40,000 kg	plants
Spinosaurus	Spined lizard	40 feet	4,000 kg	fish
Velociraptor	Fast thief	6 feet	14 kg	meat

1. How much did the dinosaur called *Maiasaura* weigh?
   a. 30 tons c. 4 tons
   b. 3,000 kg d. 40 tons

2. Which dinosaur's name means "broad lizard?"
   a. *Ankylosaurus* c. *Plateosaurus*
   b. *Eoraptor* d. *Spinosaurus*

3. How many feet long was the dinosaur called *Velociraptor*?
   a. 3 feet c. 25 feet
   b. 6 feet d. 30 feet

4. Which of these dinosaurs ate fish?
   a. *Ankylosaurus* c. *Velociraptor*
   b. *Maiasaura* d. *Spinosaurus*

5. Which is the largest, heaviest dinosaur listed in the chart?
   a. *Seismosaurus* c. *Eoraptor*
   b. *Plateosaurus* d. *Baryonyx*

Wagon Train

Will and Kate thought it would be a great adventure to travel west with the wagon train. In the spring of 1880, their family left their home in Pennsylvania and joined a wagon train headed for California. For months, their only home was the wagon. A large canvas was spread over metal hoops on top of the wagon to make a roof. Will helped his father oil the canvas so that the rain would slide off and keep them dry inside. Each day Kate and Will gathered wood as they walked beside the wagon. In the evening when the wagons stopped, Kate and her mother built a campfire for cooking supper. They hauled supplies with them so that they could cook beans and biscuits. Sometimes the men went hunting and brought back fresh deer meat or a rabbit for stew. When it rained for several days, the roads were so muddy that the wagons got stuck. There was always danger of snakes and bad weather. There were rivers and mountains to cross. There was no doctor to take care of those who got sick or injured. Will and Kate were right. Traveling with a wagon train was a great adventure, but it was a very hard life.

Unscramble the words to make a complete sentence that tells the main idea.

wagon dangerous. on a Life hard and was train ________________________________

____

Choose a word from the wagon to complete each detail.

1. ___ ___ ___ ___ ___ ___ **the canvas**
2. ___ ___ ___ ___ ___ ___ ___ ___ ___ **wood**
3. ___ ___ ___ ___ ___ ___ ___ **over a campfire**
4. ___ ___ ___ ___ ___ ___ ___ **supplies**
5. ___ ___ ___ ___ ___ ___ ___ **for meat**
6. ___ ___ ___ ___ ___ ___ ___ ___ **out for snakes**
7. ___ ___ ___ ___ ___ ___ ___ **for the rain to stop**
8. ___ ___ ___ ___ ___ ___ ___ ___ **rivers and mountains**
9. ___ ___ ___ ___ ___ ___ ___ **sick or hurt with no doctor to help**

Timothy the Tiger

Timothy the tiger is a weight lifter and he loves to look at himself in the mirror. Only one of the reflections below is his real mirror image. Can you figure out which one it is and circle it? To check your answer, do the multiplication problems below each tiger. The product that matches the number under Timothy is his exact mirror image.

214
x 36

407
x 22

563
x 17

505
x 18

499
x 12

486
x 13

107
x 34

386
x 24

719
x 12

802
x 11

272
x 19

315
x 22

189
x 41

106
x 53

610
x 11

The Math Contest

Story elements *are the different parts of a story. The* **characters** *are the people, animals, or animated objects in the story. The* **setting** *is the place and time in which the story takes place. The* **plot** *of the story includes the events and often includes a* **problem** *and a* **solution***.*

Every Friday, Mr Jefferson, the maths teacher, held a contest for his students. Sometimes they played maths baseball. Sometimes they had maths relays with flash cards. Other times, they were handed a sheet of paper with a hundred multiplication problems on it. The student who finished fastest with the most correct answers won the contest. One Friday, there was a maths bee. It was similar to a spelling bee, except the students worked math problems in their heads. There was fierce competition, until finally, everyone was out of the game except Riley and Rhonda. Mr Jefferson challenged them with problem after problem, but both students continued to answer correctly every time. It was almost time for class to end, so Mr.Jefferson gave them the same difficult problem. They had to work it in their heads. Riley thought hard and answered, "20." Rhonda answered, "18." Finally they had a winner!

To find out who won the game, work the problem below in your head. Write the answer on the blank.

$$6 + 4 + 6 - 4 - 4 + 6 + 6 = \_\_\_\_\_\_$$

Now, to see if you are correct, circle only the 6's and 4's in the box. The answer will appear.

7	4	6	5	3	1	2	6	4	8	0
6	9	1	4	3	5	6	2	8	6	7
5	0	8	6	0	4	9	7	3	1	4
3	1	7	4	0	6	5	8	7	2	6
7	0	6	5	8	4	9	3	2	9	6
8	4	9	8	0	6	1	5	7	8	4
6	2	7	3	9	2	4	8	1	6	5
6	4	4	6	1	9	0	6	6	2	3

Answer each question below.

1. **Name the three people in the story. ____________________, ________________ and ____________________**

2. **Circle where the story takes place.**
   a. in the gym **b. in the cafeteria** **c. in Mr. Jefferson's classroom**

3. **Circle the problem in the story.**
   a. Mr. Jefferson held the contest on Thursday.
   b. Class was almost over and the contest was still tied.
   c. Riley and Rhonda both answered incorrectly.

4. **Who answered the difficult question correctly? ____________**

It's All the Same!

Equivalent fractions *have the same amount.*

$\frac{1}{2} = \frac{4}{8}$

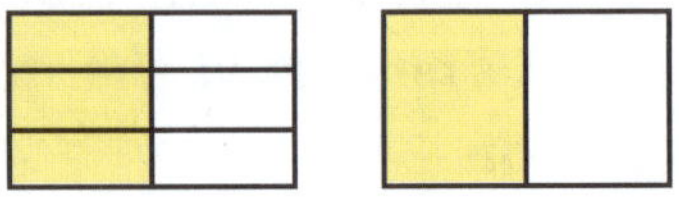

$\frac{3}{6} = \frac{1}{2}$

Write each missing numerator to show equivalent fractions.

A.

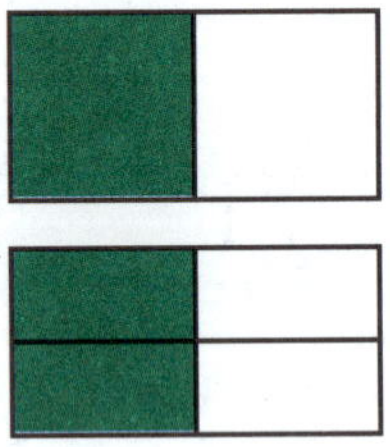

$\frac{1}{2} = \frac{\quad}{4}$

B.

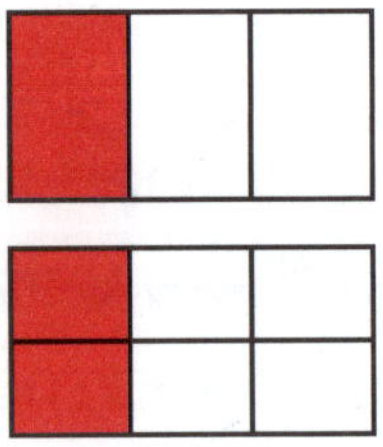

$\frac{1}{3} = \frac{\quad}{6}$

C.

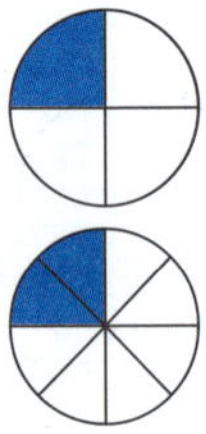

$\frac{1}{4} = \frac{\quad}{8}$

D.

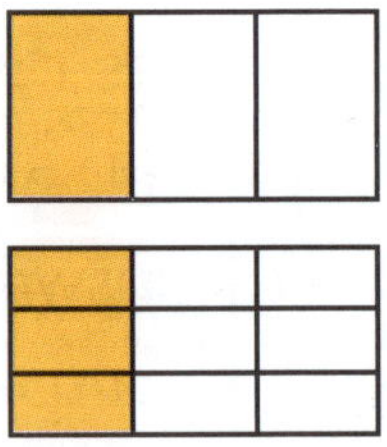

$\frac{1}{3} = \frac{\quad}{9}$

E.

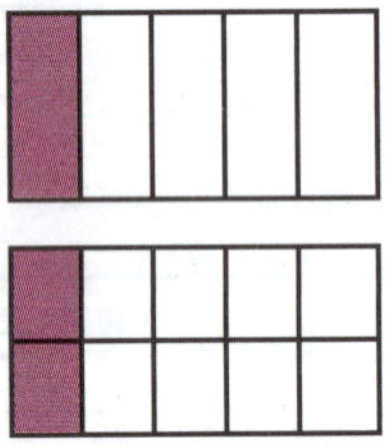

$\frac{1}{5} = \frac{\quad}{10}$

F.

$\frac{1}{2} = \frac{\quad}{8}$

G.

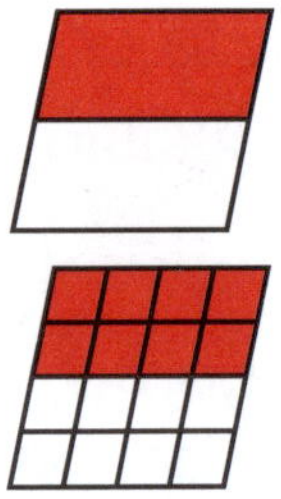

$\frac{1}{2} = \frac{\quad}{16}$

H.

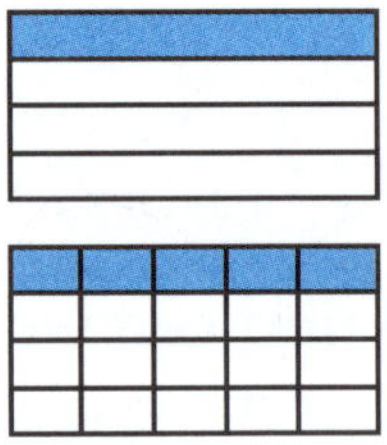

$\frac{1}{4} = \frac{\quad}{20}$

Write the number sentence that shows each set of equivalent fractions.

I.

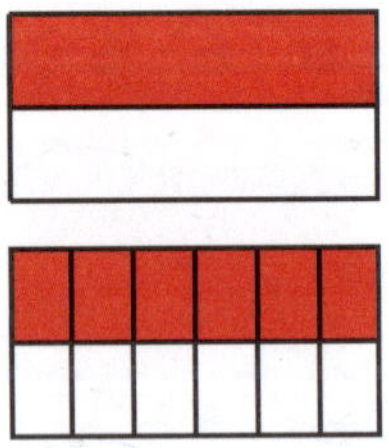

— = —

J.

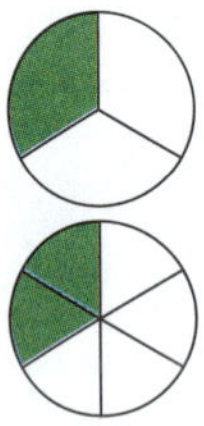

— = —

K.

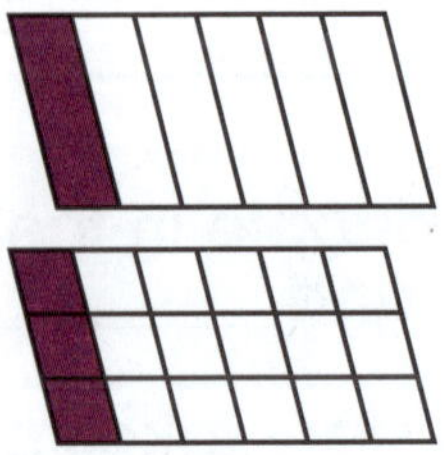

— = —

L.

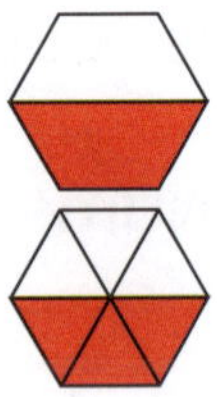

— = —

Raymond's pizza has been cut into fourths. Debbie's pizza has been cut into eighths. Raymond eats 2/4 of his pizza. Debbie eats 4/8 of her pizza. Did they eat the same amount of pizza? On another sheet of paper, draw a picture to show your answer.